Contents

*C = copper; B = bronze; S = silver; T = teacher; ( ) = the line must be played but cannot be assessed for a Medal.

Two's Company

Paul Archibald

Donkey Ride

Nick Breeze

AB 3033

Lament for a Lost Yak

Andrew Tyrrell

This Old Canon

(after 'This Old Man')

Trad. arr. Nick Breeze

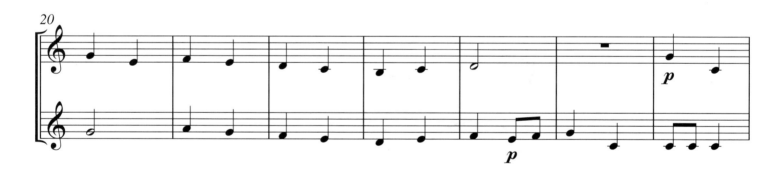

AB 3033

Dancing Shadows

Stephen Roberts

AB 3033

Lean on Me

Bill Withers arr. Chris Batchelor

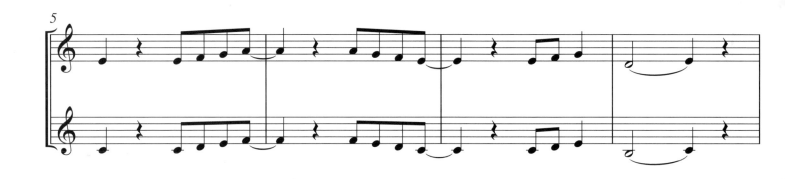

AB 3033

Bells

Nick Breeze

Rhumba for Two

Nick Breeze

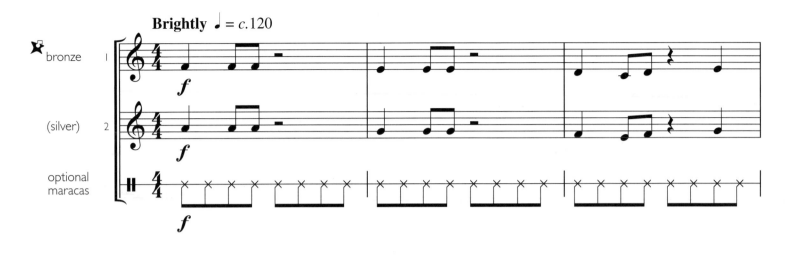

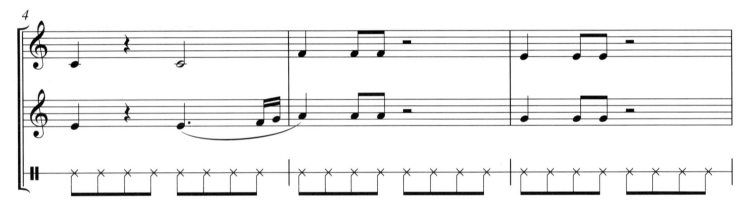

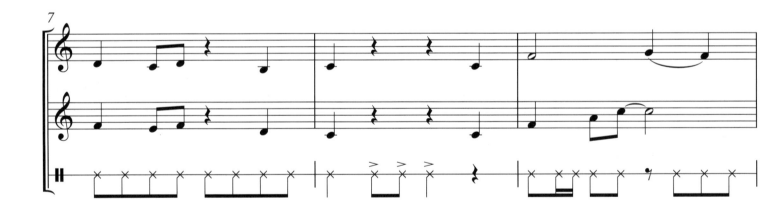

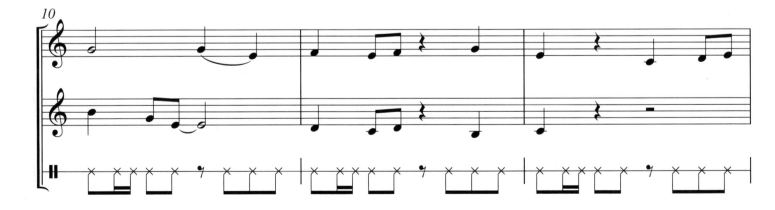

AB 3033

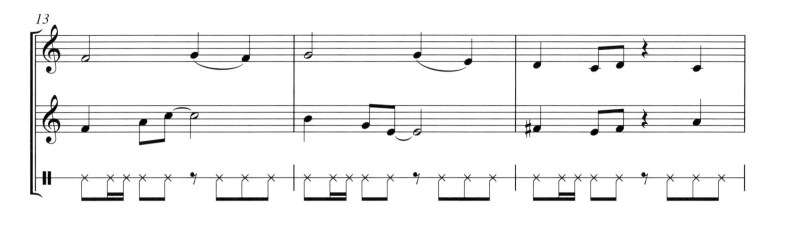

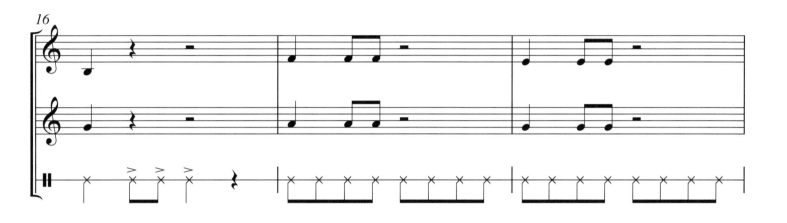

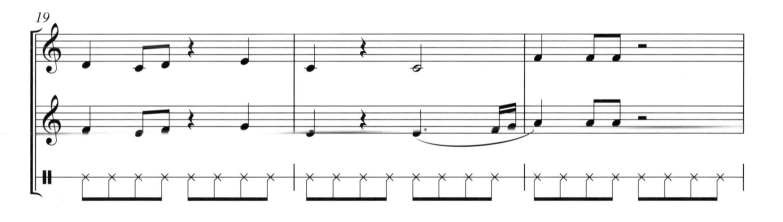

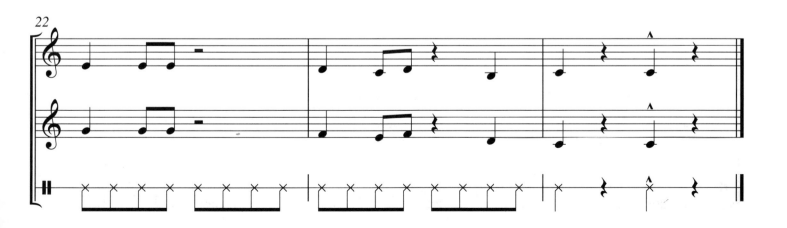

Circus Clowns

Stephen Roberts

AB 3033

Follow Me

Alan Hutt

Three in Three

Nigel Mainard

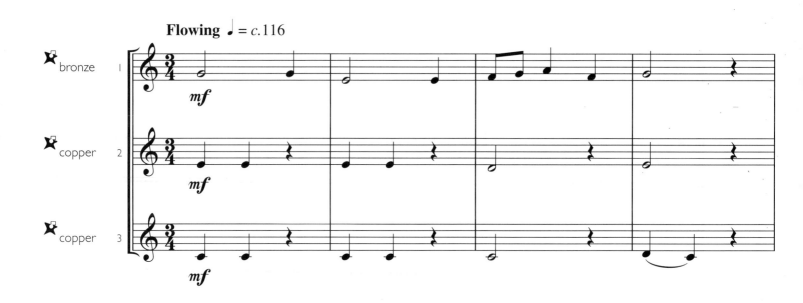

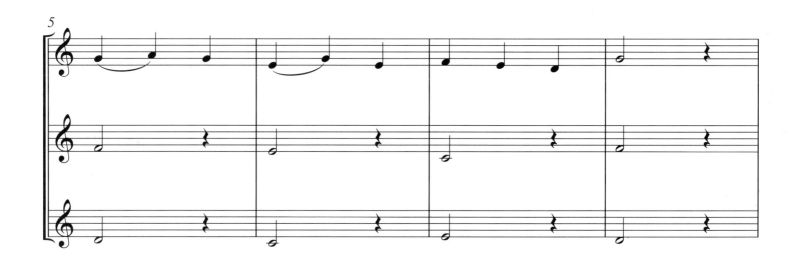

AB 3033

Stir It Up

Bob Marley arr. Chris Batchelor

Festive Fanfare

Paul Harris

AB 3033

Kum Ba Yah

Trad. African arr. John Miller

AB 3033

15

Lullaby for Nina

Andrew Tyrrell

AB 3033

Balloons

Adrian Taylor

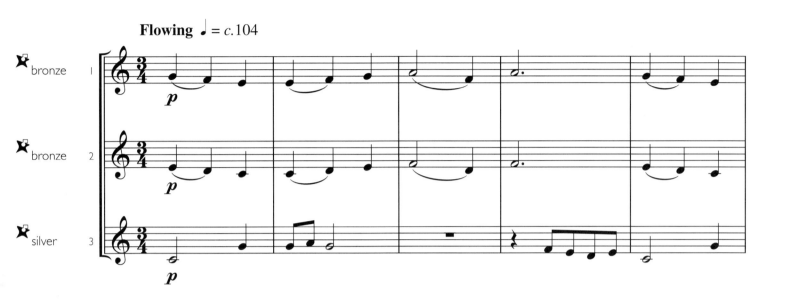

Old MacDonald

Trad. arr. John Miller

AB 3033

Folksong

Alan Hutt

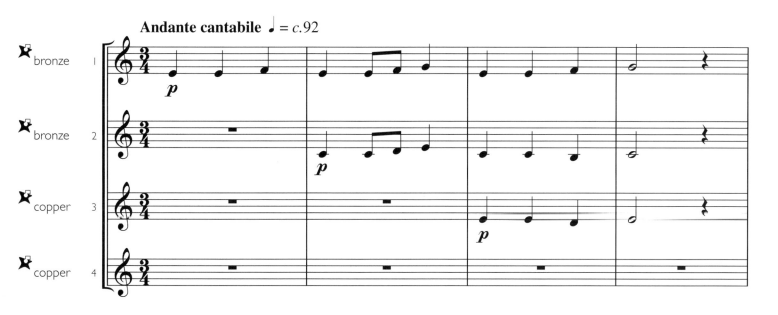

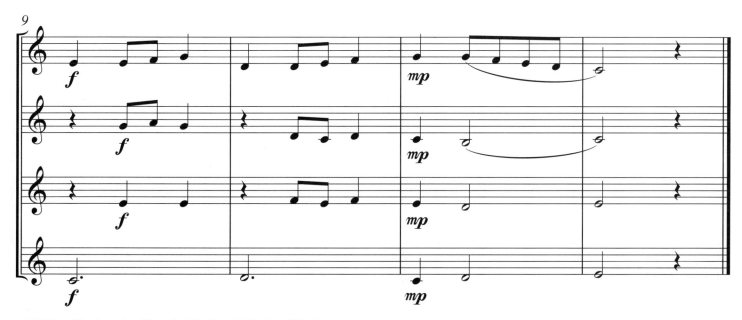

Favourite Breakfast

Nigel Mainard

* Alternative words (that fit the rhythm) can be substituted to describe your 'favourite breakfast'.

　　　　　　　　　　　AB 3033

Elephants' March

Adrian Taylor

Fanfare for a King

Adrian Taylor

AB 3033

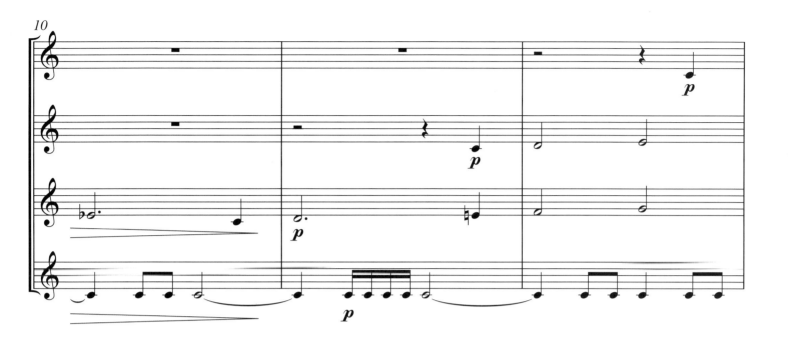

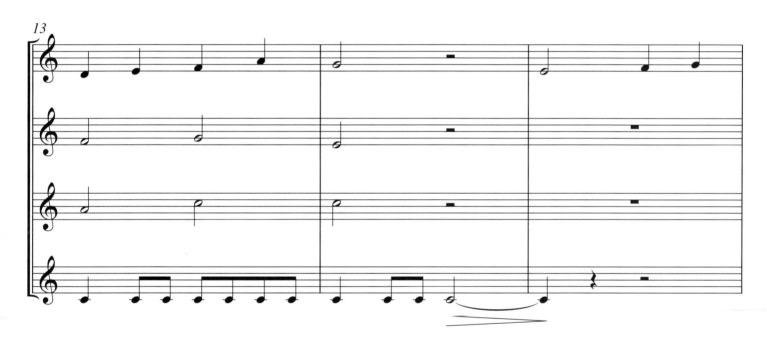

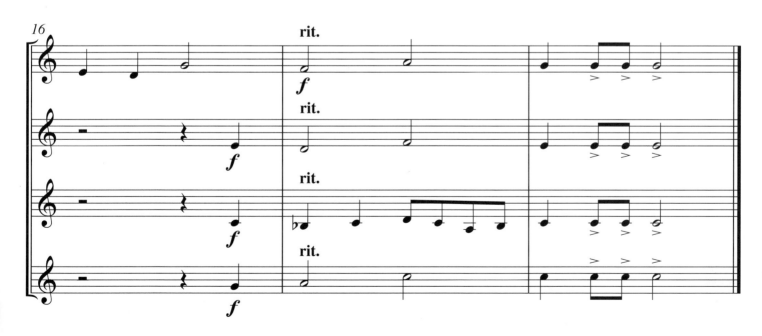

Pass the Parcel

John Frith

AB 3033